This book is dedicated to
Oliver Zhao Dash,
already a world explorer,
born on 9th July 2013
in the Year of the Snake.

Love Finse

THIS BOOK
BELONGS TO

_____

_____

"Finse Explores China"

The right of Karine Hagen to be identified as the author
and Suzy-Jane Tanner to be identified as the illustrator
of this work has been asserted by them in accordance
with the Copyright Designs and Patents Act 1988.

Text copyright © Karine Hagen 2014
Illustrations copyright © Suzy-Jane Tanner 2014

First published by Viking Cruises 2014. Reprinted 2016
83 Wimbledon Park Side, London, SW19 5LP

ISBN 978-1-909968-04-2

www.finse.me

Produced by Colophon Digital Projects Ltd,
Old Isleworth, TW7 6RJ, United Kingdom
Printed in China.

FINSE
EXPLORES CHINA

Karine Hagen
Suzy-Jane Tanner

Xian

Yangtze

Shibaozhai

Chongqing

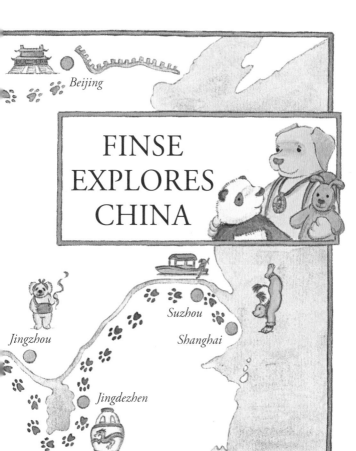

Beijing

FINSE
EXPLORES
CHINA

Jingzhou

Suzhou

Shanghai

Jingdezhen

I remember teatime at Highclere Castle, my puppyhood home.

We have an old Chinese red lacquer tea chest in the drawing room. Mummy explained that tea plants originally grew in China. I decided to go there to explore.

China is an ancient civilization with the world's largest population.

In Shanghai I enjoyed delicious Chinese food. It took me some time to learn to eat with chopsticks!

After supper there was a performance by Shanghai's famous acrobats.

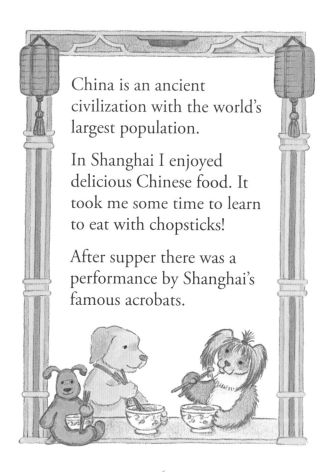

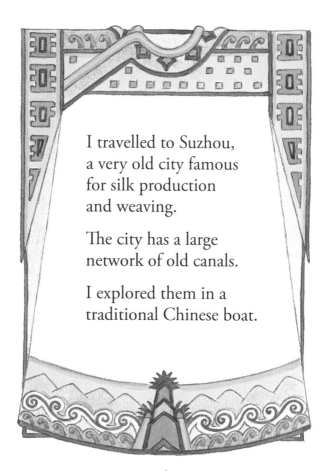

I travelled to Suzhou,
a very old city famous
for silk production
and weaving.

The city has a large
network of old canals.

I explored them in a
traditional Chinese boat.

Health and well-being
are important in China.

Plants, herbs and
acupuncture have been
used over the centuries
in traditional
Chinese medicine.

I took part in morning
Tai Chi exercises in
the park.

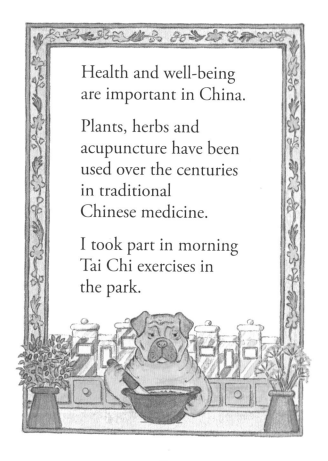

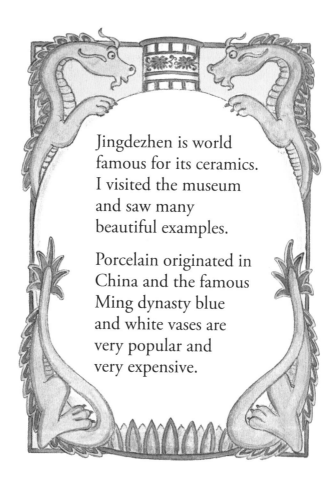

Jingdezhen is world
famous for its ceramics.
I visited the museum
and saw many
beautiful examples.

Porcelain originated in
China and the famous
Ming dynasty blue
and white vases are
very popular and
very expensive.

Along the Yangtze there are several elementary schools, sponsored by Viking Cruises.

I visited one and helped the puppies with their language class. Then I watched their lively dance performance.

15

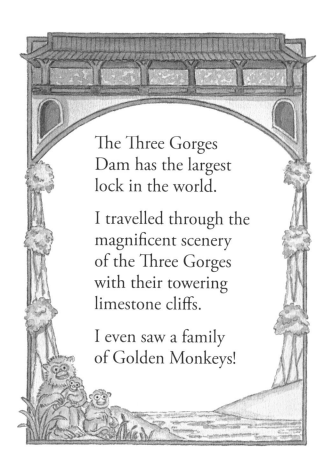

The Three Gorges Dam has the largest lock in the world.

I travelled through the magnificent scenery of the Three Gorges with their towering limestone cliffs.

I even saw a family of Golden Monkeys!

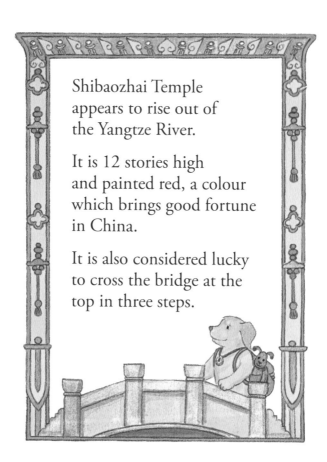

Shibaozhai Temple appears to rise out of the Yangtze River.

It is 12 stories high and painted red, a colour which brings good fortune in China.

It is also considered lucky to cross the bridge at the top in three steps.

19

There are giant
pandas and their cubs
at the famous
Chongqing Zoo.

Pandas only eat bamboo
shoots and leaves.

When they are not
eating, they play
and sleep.

In Xian, I admired the Terracotta Army, a group of 8000 fierce life-sized soldiers, built for Emperor Qin Shi Huang over 2000 years ago.

Every sculpture is unique and every one was found broken. This must be the world's biggest jigsaw puzzle!

In the Badaling Hills,
I walked along part of
the Great Wall of China.

Building started in
ancient times and
continued over
many centuries.

The entire wall now
measures over 13000
miles long, stretching
from the desert to the sea.

For almost 500 years, the Forbidden City in Beijing was the home of the Chinese emperors.

I watched a performance by the Peking Opera, a form of traditional Chinese theatre.

The actors wear brightly coloured costumes and masks or lots of make-up.

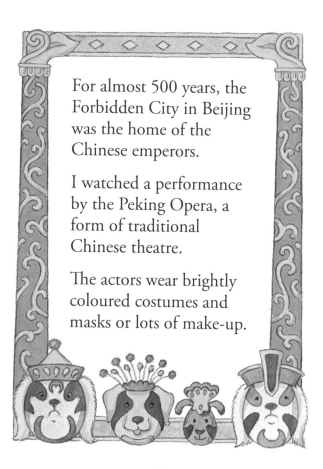

THE CHINESE ZODIAC

Which animal year were you born in?
Approximate since China follows the lunar year

Monkey	1944, 1956, 1968, 1980, 1992, 2004
	Clever & fun loving but cunning
Rooster	1945, 1957, 1969, 1981, 1993, 2005
	Hardworking & smart but tactless
Dog	1946, 1958, 1970, 1982, 1994, 2006
	Loyal & generous but critical
Pig	1947, 1959, 1971, 1983, 1995, 2007
	Affectionate & shy but vain
Rat	1948, 1960, 1972, 1984, 1996, 2008
	Charming & imaginative but selfish
Ox	1949, 1961, 1973, 1985, 1997, 2009
	Strong & patient but stubborn
Tiger	1950, 1962, 1974, 1986, 1998, 2010
	Optimistic & brave but obstinate
Rabbit	1951, 1963, 1975, 1987, 1999, 2011
	Home loving & kind but impatient
Dragon	1952, 1964, 1976, 1988, 2000, 2012
	Charismatic & intelligent but proud
Snake	1953, 1965, 1977, 1989, 2001, 2013
	Wise & witty but suspicious
Horse	1954, 1966, 1978. 1990, 2002, 2014
	Positive & friendly but nosy
Goat	1955, 1967, 1979, 1991, 2003, 2015
	Creative & elegant but hesitant

All through my journey, I admired the beautiful Chinese calligraphy.

I even had a chance to try my paw!

Goodbye China!
Zài jiàn!
再见

DOGOLOGY

Finse enjoyed meeting the charming and unusual dogs of China and some other animals too!